TODAY'S PRAYER

Lord
TEACH ME TO...

PRAYER REQUESTS

Rejoiceth not in
iniquity, but rejoiceth
in the truth.

1 Corinthians 13:6

Date:

TODAY'S PRAYER

Lord TEACH ME TO...

PRAYER REQUESTS

Blessed be the God and Father of our Lord Jesus Christ, which according to his abundant mercy hath begotten us again unto a lively hope by the resurrection of Jesus Christ from the dead.

1 Peter 1:3

Date:

TODAY'S PRAYER

Lord
TEACH ME TO...

PRAYER REQUESTS

I will bless the Lord at all times: his praise shall continually be in my mouth.

Psalm 34:1

Date:

TODAY'S PRAYER

Lord
TEACH ME TO...

PRAYER REQUESTS

I will sing unto the Lord as long as I live: I will sing praise to my God while I have my being.

Psalm 104:33

Date:

TODAY'S PRAYER

Lord
TEACH ME TO...

PRAYER REQUESTS

I will praise thee, for I am fearfully and wonderfully made: marvellous are thy works.
Psalm 139:14

Date:

TODAY'S PRAYER

Lord
TEACH ME TO...

PRAYER REQUESTS

He shall cover thee
with his feathers, and
under his wings shalt
thou trust.

Psalm 91:4 a

Date:

TODAY'S PRAYER

Lord
TEACH ME TO...

PRAYER REQUESTS

We love him, because
he first loved us.

1 John 4:19

Date.

TODAY'S PRAYER

Lord
TEACH ME TO...

PRAYER REQUESTS

Trust in the Lord with all thine heart; and lean not unto thine own understanding.
Proverbs 3:5

Date:

TODAY'S PRAYER

Lord
TEACH ME TO...

PRAYER REQUESTS

For the day is near, even the day of the Lord is near, a cloudy day; it shall be the time of the heathen.

Ezekiel 30:3

Date:

TODAY'S PRAYER

Lord
TEACH ME TO...

PRAYER REQUESTS

But the Lord is
with me as a mighty
terrible one

Jeremiah 20:11

Date.

TODAY'S PRAYER

Lord
TEACH ME TO...

PRAYER REQUESTS

For whither thou goest,
I will go; and where thou
lodgest, I will lodge:
thy people shall be my people,
and thy God my God.

Ruth 1:16 b

Date:

TODAY'S PRAYER

Lord
TEACH ME TO...

PRAYER REQUESTS

Nor height, nor depth, nor any other creature, shall be able to separate us from the love of God, which is in Christ Jesus our Lord.

Romans 8:39

Date:

TODAY'S PRAYER

Lord
TEACH ME TO...

PRAYER REQUESTS

Now unto him that is able to do exceeding abundantly above all that we ask or think, according to the power that worketh in us.

Ephesians 3:20

Date:

TODAY'S PRAYER

_____
_____
_____
_____
_____
_____
_____
_____
_____
_____
_____
_____
_____
_____
_____
_____

Lord
TEACH ME TO...

_____
_____
_____
_____

PRAYER REQUESTS

_____
_____
_____
_____
_____
_____
_____
_____
_____
_____
_____

behold, I have set
before thee an open door,
and no man can shut it.

Revelation 3:8 a

Date:

TODAY'S PRAYER

Lord
TEACH ME TO...

For I reckon that the sufferings of this present time are not worthy to be compared with the glory which shall be revealed in us.

Romans 8:18

Prayer Requests

Date

TODAY'S PRAYER

Lord
TEACH ME TO...

Prayer Requests

Be ye angry, and sin not: let not the sun go down upon your wrath.

Ephesians 4:26

Date:

TODAY'S PRAYER

Lord
TEACH ME TO...

PRAYER REQUESTS

His truth
shall be thy shield
and buckler.

Psalm 91:4 b

Date.

TODAY'S PRAYER

_____
_____
_____
_____
_____
_____
_____
_____
_____
_____
_____
_____
_____
_____
_____
_____

Lord
TEACH ME TO...

_____
_____
_____
_____

For my yoke is easy,
and my burden is light.

Matthew 11:30

PRAYER REQUESTS

_____
_____
_____
_____
_____
_____
_____
_____
_____
_____
_____

Date:

TODAY'S PRAYER

Lord
TEACH ME TO...

PRAYER REQUESTS

I can do all things through Christ which strengtheneth me.

Philippians 4:13

Date.

TODAY'S PRAYER

Lord
TEACH ME TO...

Repent ye therefore, and be converted, that your sins may be blotted out, when the times of refreshing shall come from the presence of the Lord.

Acts 3:19

PRAYER REQUESTS

Date:

TODAY'S PRAYER

Lord
TEACH ME TO...

PRAYER REQUESTS

Being confident of this very
thing, that he which hath
begun a good work in you
will perform it until the
day of Jesus Christ.

Philippians 1:6

Date:

TODAY'S PRAYER

Lord TEACH ME TO...

PRAYER REQUESTS

He hath shewed thee, O man, what is good; and what doth the Lord require of thee, but to do justly, and to love mercy, and to walk humbly with thy God?

Micah 6:8

Date.

TODAY'S PRAYER

Lord TEACH ME TO...

And he spake a parable unto them to this end, that men ought always to pray, and not to faint.

Luke 18:1

Prayer Requests

Date:

TODAY'S PRAYER

Lord
TEACH ME TO...

PRAYER REQUESTS

The heavens declare
the glory of God;
and the firmament
sheweth his handywork.

Psalm 19:1

Date:

TODAY'S PRAYER

_____
_____
_____
_____
_____
_____
_____
_____
_____
_____
_____
_____
_____
_____
_____
_____
_____
_____
_____

Lord
TEACH ME TO...

_____
_____
_____
_____
_____

Which hope we have as an anchor of the soul, both sure and stedfast, and which entereth into that within the veil.

Hebrews 6:19

Prayer Requests

_____
_____
_____
_____
_____
_____
_____
_____

Date:

TODAY'S PRAYER

Lord
TEACH ME TO...

PRAYER REQUESTS

The Lord shall fight
for you, and ye shall
hold your peace.

Exodus 14:14

Date:

TODAY'S PRAYER

Lord
TEACH ME TO...

Keep thy heart with all diligence, for out of it are the issues of life.

Proverbs 4:23

Prayer Requests

Date.

Lord
TEACH ME TO...

PRAYER REQUESTS

What shall we then
say to these things?
If God be for us, who
can be against us?

Romans 8:31

Date:

TODAY'S PRAYER

Lord
TEACH ME TO...

But godliness with
contentment is
great gain.

1 Timothy 6:6

PRAYER REQUESTS

Date.

TODAY'S PRAYER

Lord
TEACH ME TO...

To every thing there is a season, and a time to every purpose under the heaven.

Ecclesiastes 3:1

PRAYER REQUESTS

Date:

TODAY'S PRAYER

Lord
TEACH ME TO…

PRAYER REQUESTS

But we believe that through the grace of the Lord Jesus Christ we shall be saved, even as they.

Acts 15:11

Date:

TODAY'S PRAYER

Lord
TEACH ME TO...

PRAYER REQUESTS

A new heart also will I give you, and a new spirit will I put within you: and I will take away the stony heart out of your flesh, and I will give you an heart of flesh.

Ezekiel 36:26

Date:

TODAY'S PRAYER

Lord
TEACH ME TO...

Prayer Requests

If any of you lack wisdom,
let him ask of God, that
giveth to all men liberally,
and upbraideth not;
and it shall be given him.

James 1:5

Date:

TODAY'S PRAYER

Lord
TEACH ME TO...

PRAYER REQUESTS

And be ye kind one to another, tenderhearted, forgiving one another, even as God for Christ's sake hath forgiven you.

Ephesians 4:32

Date.

TODAY'S PRAYER

Lord
TEACH ME TO...

Prayer Requests

Be not deceived;
God is not mocked: for
whatsoever a man soweth,
that shall he also reap.

Galatians 6:7

Date.

TODAY'S PRAYER

Lord
TEACH ME TO...

PRAYER REQUESTS

Fear not: for I have
redeemed thee, I have
called thee by thy name;
thou art mine.

Isaiah 43:1

Date:

TODAY'S PRAYER

Lord
TEACH ME TO...

*For this child I prayed,
and the Lord hath given
me my petition which
I asked of him.*

1 Samuel 1:27

PRAYER REQUESTS

Date:

TODAY'S PRAYER

Lord
TEACH ME TO...

PRAYER REQUESTS

For this cause shall a man
leave his father and mother,
and shall be joined unto his wife,
and they two shall be one flesh.

Ephesians 5:31

Date:

TODAY'S PRAYER

Lord
TEACH ME TO...

If we say that we have no sin, we deceive ourselves, and the truth is not in us.

1 John 1:8

PRAYER REQUESTS

Date:

TODAY'S PRAYER

Lord TEACH ME TO...

PRAYER REQUESTS

But he was wounded for our transgressions, he was bruised for our iniquities

Isaiah 53:5

Date:

TODAY'S PRAYER

Lord
TEACH ME TO...

PRAYER REQUESTS

I am with you always,
even unto the end
of the world.

Matthew 28:20

Date:

TODAY'S PRAYER

Lord
TEACH ME TO...

PRAYER REQUESTS

These things I have spoken unto you,
that in me ye might have peace.
In the world ye shall have
tribulation: but be of good cheer;
I have overcome the world.

John 16:33

Date:

TODAY'S PRAYER

Lord
TEACH ME TO...

My little children, these things write I unto you, that ye sin not. And if any man sin, we have an advocate with the Father, Jesus Christ the righteous.

1 John 2:1

PRAYER REQUESTS

Date:

TODAY'S PRAYER

Lord
TEACH ME TO...

PRAYER REQUESTS

Those things, which ye have
both learned, and received,
and heard, and seen in me,
do: and the God of
peace shall be with you.

Philippians 4:9

Date:

TODAY'S PRAYER

Lord
TEACH ME TO...

PRAYER REQUESTS

It is of the Lord's mercies that we are not consumed, because his compassions fail not. They are new every morning: great is thy faithfulness.

Lamentations 3:22-23

Date:

TODAY'S PRAYER

Lord TEACH ME TO...

PRAYER REQUESTS

Ye have not chosen me, but I have chosen you, and ordained you, that ye should go and bring forth fruit, and that your fruit should remain: that whatsoever ye shall ask of the Father in my name, he may give it you.

John 15:16

Date:

TODAY'S PRAYER

Lord
TEACH ME TO...

And she shall bring forth a
son, and thou shalt call his name
Jesus: for he shall save his
people from their sins.

Matthew 1:21

PRAYER REQUESTS

Date:

TODAY'S PRAYER

Lord TEACH ME TO...

PRAYER REQUESTS

*For thou art my lamp,
O Lord: and the Lord
will lighten my darkness.*

2 Samuel 22:29

Date:

TODAY'S PRAYER

Lord
TEACH ME TO...

God is in the midst of her;
she shall not be moved:
God shall help her, and
that right early.

Psalm 46:5

PRAYER REQUESTS

Date:

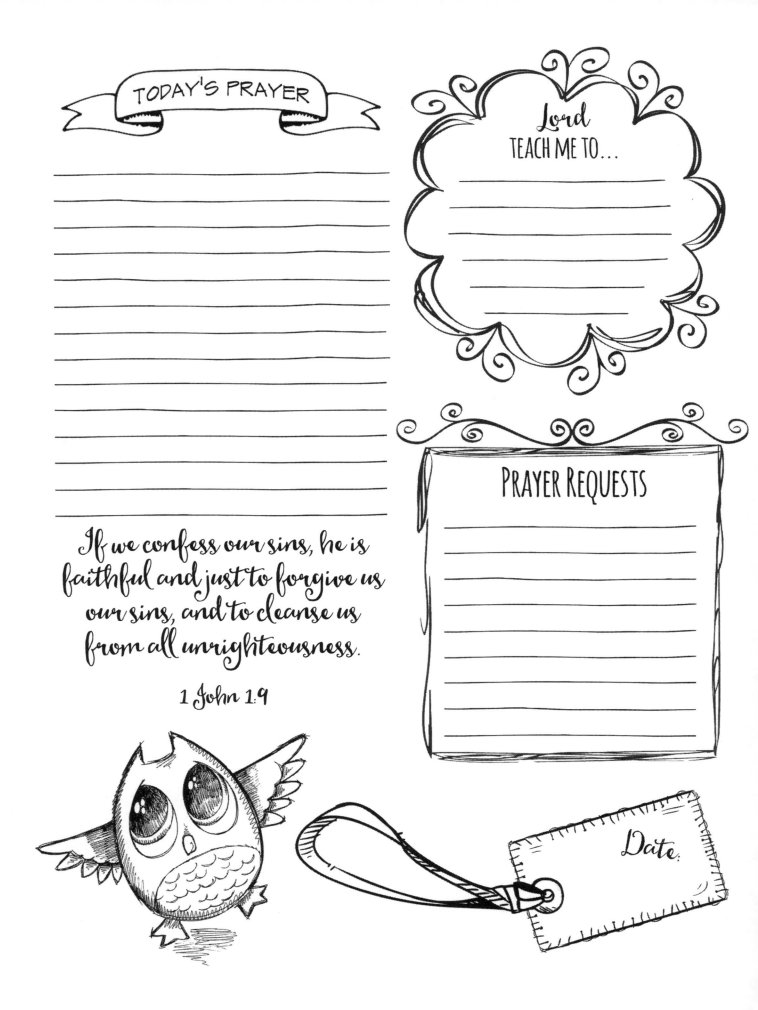

TODAY'S PRAYER

Lord
TEACH ME TO...

If we confess our sins, he is faithful and just to forgive us our sins, and to cleanse us from all unrighteousness.

1 John 1:9

PRAYER REQUESTS

Date:

TODAY'S PRAYER

Lord
TEACH ME TO...

Blessed are the pure
in heart: for they
shall see God.

Matthew 5:8

Prayer Requests

Date.

TODAY'S PRAYER

Lord TEACH ME TO...

He that loveth not
knoweth not God;
for God is love.

1 John 4:8

PRAYER REQUESTS

Date:

TODAY'S PRAYER

Lord
TEACH ME TO...

PRAYER REQUESTS

Fear thou not; for I am with thee: be not dismayed; for I am thy God.

Isaiah 41:10 a

Date:

TODAY'S PRAYER

Lord
TEACH ME TO...

PRAYER REQUESTS

Neither is there salvation
in any other: for there
is none other name under
heaven given among men,
whereby we must be saved.

Acts 4:12

Date:

TODAY'S PRAYER

Lord TEACH ME TO...

PRAYER REQUESTS

Pleasant words are as an honeycomb, sweet to the soul, and health to the bones.

Proverbs 16:24

Date:

TODAY'S PRAYER

Lord
TEACH ME TO...

PRAYER REQUESTS

The desire of a man is his
kindness: and a poor man is
better than a liar.

Proverbs 19:22

Date:

Lord
TEACH ME TO...

PRAYER REQUESTS

Blessed is the
man that endureth
temptation.

James 1:12 a

Date:

Lord
TEACH ME TO...

Prayer Requests

*Wherefore, my beloved brethren,
let every man be swift to hear,
slow to speak, slow to wrath.*

James 1:19

Date

TODAY'S PRAYER

Lord
TEACH ME TO...

And he rode upon a
cherub, and did fly: and
he was seen upon the wings
of the wind.

2 Samuel 22:11

Prayer Requests

Date:

TODAY'S PRAYER

Lord
TEACH ME TO...

PRAYER REQUESTS

Thou art worthy, O Lord, to receive glory and honour and power: for thou hast created all things, and for thy pleasure they are and were created.

Revelation 4:11

Date:

TODAY'S PRAYER

Lord
TEACH ME TO...

PRAYER REQUESTS

Let your conversation be without covetousness; and be content with such things as ye have: for he hath said, I will never leave thee, nor forsake thee.

Hebrews 13:5

Date:

TODAY'S PRAYER

Lord
TEACH ME TO...

Casting all your
care upon him;
for he careth for you.

1 Peter 5:7

Prayer Requests

Date:

TODAY'S PRAYER

Lord
TEACH ME TO...

PRAYER REQUESTS

Be strong and of a
good courage, fear not,
nor be afraid of them

Deuteronomy 31:6 a

Date:

TODAY'S PRAYER

Lord
TEACH ME TO...

Give thanks unto the Lord,
call upon his name,
make known his deeds
among the people.

1 Chronicles 16:8

PRAYER REQUESTS

Date:

TODAY'S PRAYER

Lord
TEACH ME TO...

And the Lord shall deliver me from every evil work, and will preserve me unto his heavenly kingdom.

2 Timothy 4:18 a

PRAYER REQUESTS

Date:

TODAY'S PRAYER

Lord
TEACH ME TO...

PRAYER REQUESTS

But God commendeth his
love toward us, in that,
while we were yet sinners,
Christ died for us.

Romans 5:8

Date:

TODAY'S PRAYER

Lord TEACH ME TO...

And when ye stand praying, forgive, if ye have ought against any: that your Father also which is in heaven may forgive you your trespasses.

Mark 11:25

PRAYER REQUESTS

Date:

TODAY'S PRAYER

Lord
TEACH ME TO...

PRAYER REQUESTS

As soon as Jesus heard the word that was spoken, he saith unto the ruler of the synagogue, Be not afraid, only believe.

Mark 5:36

Date

TODAY'S PRAYER

Lord
TEACH ME TO...

All scripture is given by inspiration of God, and is profitable for doctrine, for reproof, for correction, for instruction in righteousness.

2 Timothy 3:16

PRAYER REQUESTS

Date:

TODAY'S PRAYER

Lord
TEACH ME TO...

PRAYER REQUESTS

My heart rejoiceth in the Lord.

1 Samuel 2:1

Date:

TODAY'S PRAYER

Lord
TEACH ME TO...

PRAYER REQUESTS

Jesus answered and said
unto him, What I do thou
knowest not now; but thou
shalt know hereafter.

John 13:7

Date:

TODAY'S PRAYER

Lord
TEACH ME TO...

PRAYER REQUESTS

But Jesus beheld them,
and said unto them,
With men this is impossible;
but with God all things
are possible.

Matthew 19:26

Date:

TODAY'S PRAYER

Lord
TEACH ME TO...

PRAYER REQUESTS

I live by the faith of the
Son of God, who loved me,
and gave himself for me.
Galatians 2:20 b

Date:

TODAY'S PRAYER

Lord
TEACH ME TO...

PRAYER REQUESTS

for the Lord thy God,
he it is that doth go with
thee; he will not fail thee,
nor forsake thee.

Deuteronomy 31:6 b

Date:

TODAY'S PRAYER

Lord
TEACH ME TO...

Every good gift and every perfect gift is from above, and cometh down from the Father of lights, with whom is no variableness, neither shadow of turning.

James 1:17

PRAYER REQUESTS

Date:

TODAY'S PRAYER

Lord
TEACH ME TO...

PRAYER REQUESTS

For even hereunto were ye
called: because Christ also
suffered for us, leaving
us an example, that ye
should follow his steps.

1 Peter 2:21

Date:

TODAY'S PRAYER

Lord
TEACH ME TO...

This is my commandment,
That ye love one another,
as I have loved you.

John 15:12

Prayer Requests

Date.

TODAY'S PRAYER

Lord
TEACH ME TO...

Comfort your hearts,
and stablish you in every
good word and work.

2 Thessalonians 2:17

PRAYER REQUESTS

Date:

TODAY'S PRAYER

Lord
TEACH ME TO...

And blessed is she that believed: for there shall be a performance of those things which were told her from the Lord.

Luke 1:45

PRAYER REQUESTS

Date:

TODAY'S PRAYER

Lord
TEACH ME TO...

PRAYER REQUESTS

Lo, children are an heritage
of the Lord: and the fruit of
the womb is his reward.

Psalm 127:3

Date:

TODAY'S PRAYER

Lord
TEACH ME TO…

PRAYER REQUESTS

Beareth all things, believeth all things, hopeth all things, endureth all things.

1 Corinthians 13:7

Date:

TODAY'S PRAYER

Lord
TEACH ME TO...

How beautiful are the
feet of them that preach the
gospel of peace, and bring
glad tidings of good things!

Romans 10:15

PRAYER REQUESTS

Date:

Lord
TEACH ME TO...

In him was life, and
the life was the
light of men.

John 1:4

Prayer Requests

Date:

TODAY'S PRAYER

Lord
TEACH ME TO...

And now,
Lord, what wait I for?
my hope is in thee.

Psalm 39:7

PRAYER REQUESTS

Date:

TODAY'S PRAYER

Lord
TEACH ME TO...

Prayer Requests

Rejoicing in hope, patient
in tribulation, continuing
instant in prayer.

Romans 12:12

Date

TODAY'S PRAYER

Lord
TEACH ME TO...

PRAYER REQUESTS

Let no man despise thy youth;
but be thou an example of the
believers, in word, in
conversation, in charity,
in spirit, in faith, in purity.

1 Timothy 4:12

Date:

TODAY'S PRAYER

Lord
TEACH ME TO...

And ye are complete in him,
which is the head of all
principality and power.

Colossians 2:10

Prayer Requests

Date:

TODAY'S PRAYER

Lord
TEACH ME TO…

There is no fear in love; but perfect love casteth out fear: because fear hath torment. He that feareth is not made perfect in love.

1 John 4:18

PRAYER REQUESTS

Date:

TODAY'S PRAYER

Lord TEACH ME TO...

And he said unto her,
Thy sins are forgiven.

Luke 7:48

PRAYER REQUESTS

Date:

TODAY'S PRAYER

Lord
TEACH ME TO...

Prayer Requests

And they that be wise shall shine as the brightness of the firmament; and they that turn many to righteousness as the stars for ever and ever.

Daniel 12:3

Date

TODAY'S PRAYER

Lord
TEACH ME TO...

She is more precious than
rubies: and all the things
thou canst desire are not to
be compared unto her.

Proverbs 3:15

PRAYER REQUESTS

Date:

TODAY'S PRAYER

Lord
TEACH ME TO...

Prayer Requests

But they that wait
upon the Lord shall
renew their strength.
Isaiah 40:31

Date

TODAY'S PRAYER

Lord
TEACH ME TO...

Therefore all things whatsoever ye would that men should do to you, do ye even so to them: for this is the law and the prophets.

Matthew 7:12

PRAYER REQUESTS

Date.

TODAY'S PRAYER

For we walk by faith, not by sight

2 Corinthians 5:7

Lord TEACH ME TO...

Prayer Requests

Date

TODAY'S PRAYER

Lord
TEACH ME TO...

No man hath seen God at any time. If we love one another, God dwelleth in us, and his love is perfected in us.

1 John 4:12

Prayer Requests

Date

TODAY'S PRAYER

Lord
TEACH ME TO...

And he saith unto them,
Follow me, and I will
make you fishers of men.

Matthew 4:19

PRAYER REQUESTS

Date:

TODAY'S PRAYER

Lord
TEACH ME TO...

PRAYER REQUESTS

For the Lord of hosts hath purposed, and who shall disannul it? and his hand is stretched out, and who shall turn it back?

Isaiah 14:27

Date:

TODAY'S PRAYER

Lord
TEACH ME TO...

Behold, I give unto you power to
tread on serpents and scorpions,
and over all the power of the
enemy: and nothing shall by
any means hurt you.

Luke 10:19

Prayer Requests

Date:

TODAY'S PRAYER

Lord
TEACH ME TO...

PRAYER REQUESTS

I am my beloved's,
and my beloved is mine:
he feedeth among
the lilies.

Song of Solomon 6:3

Date:

TODAY'S PRAYER

Lord TEACH ME TO...

Prayer Requests

But when ye pray, use not vain repetitions, as the heathen do: for they think that they shall be heard for their much speaking.

Matthew 6:7

Date:

TODAY'S PRAYER

Lord
TEACH ME TO...

Have not I commanded thee?
Be strong and of a good courage,
be not afraid, neither be thou
dismayed: for the Lord thy God is
with thee whithersoever thou goest.

Joshua 1:9

Prayer Requests

Date.

TODAY'S PRAYER

Lord
TEACH ME TO...

PRAYER REQUESTS

In the shadow of thy wings
will I make my refuge, until
these calamities be overpast.

Psalm 57:1

Date:

TODAY'S PRAYER

Lord
TEACH ME TO...

PRAYER REQUESTS

Thou wilt keep him in perfect peace, whose mind is stayed on thee: because he trusteth in thee.

Isaiah 26:3

Date:

TODAY'S PRAYER

Lord
TEACH ME TO...

The Lord is nigh unto them
that are of a broken heart;
and saveth such as be of
a contrite spirit.

Psalm 34:18

PRAYER REQUESTS

Date.

TODAY'S PRAYER

Lord
TEACH ME TO...

Pray
without ceasing.

1 Thessalonians 5:17

Prayer Requests

Date:

TODAY'S PRAYER

Lord
TEACH ME TO...

Fear not, little flock, for it
is your Father's good pleasure
to give you the kingdom.

Luke 12:32

Prayer Requests

Date.

TODAY'S PRAYER

Lord
TEACH ME TO...

PRAYER REQUESTS

*Strength and honour are
her clothing; and she
shall rejoice in time to come.*

Proverbs 31:25

Date:

TODAY'S PRAYER

Lord
TEACH ME TO...

But he said, Yea rather,
blessed are they that hear the
word of God, and keep it.

Luke 11:28

Prayer Requests

Date:

TODAY'S PRAYER

Lord
TEACH ME TO...

PRAYER REQUESTS

Submit yourselves
therefore to God.
Resist the devil, and he
will flee from you.

James 4:7

Date:

Lord
TEACH ME TO...

Now the end of the
commandment is charity
out of a pure heart, and
of a good conscience, and of
faith unfeigned.

1 Timothy 1:5

Prayer Requests

Date:

TODAY'S PRAYER

Lord
TEACH ME TO…

Beware of false prophets,
which come to you in sheep's
clothing, but inwardly they
are ravening wolves.

Matthew 7:15

PRAYER REQUESTS

Date:

Lord
TEACH ME TO...

PRAYER REQUESTS

If we live in the
Spirit, let us also
walk in the Spirit.

Galatians 5:25

Date:

TODAY'S PRAYER

Lord TEACH ME TO...

Be ye angry, and sin not:
let not the sun go down
upon your wrath.

Ephesians 4:26

PRAYER REQUESTS

Date:

TODAY'S PRAYER

Lord
TEACH ME TO...

*Then shalt thou call,
and the Lord shall answer;
thou shalt cry, and he shall
say, Here I am.*

Isaiah 58:9

PRAYER REQUESTS

Date

TODAY'S PRAYER

Lord
TEACH ME TO...

PRAYER REQUESTS

Jesus said unto him,
If thou canst believe, all
things are possible to
him that believeth.

Mark 9:23

Date:

TODAY'S PRAYER

Lord
TEACH ME TO...

PRAYER REQUESTS

For God hath not given us the spirit of fear; but of power, and of love, and of a sound mind.

2 Timothy 1:7

Date:

TODAY'S PRAYER

Lord
TEACH ME TO...

There are many devices
in a man's heart; nevertheless
the counsel of the Lord,
that shall stand.

Proverbs 19:21

Prayer Requests

Date:

TODAY'S PRAYER

Lord
TEACH ME TO…

PRAYER REQUESTS

The Lord is my
strength and my shield;
my heart trusted
in him, and I am helped

Psalm 28:7 a

Date:

TODAY'S PRAYER

Lord
TEACH ME TO...

PRAYER REQUESTS

In my distress
I cried unto the Lord,
and he heard me.

Psalm 120:1

Date:

TODAY'S PRAYER

Lord
TEACH ME TO...

God is my strength
and power: and he
maketh my way perfect.

2 Samuel 22:33

PRAYER REQUESTS

Date:

TODAY'S PRAYER

Lord
TEACH ME TO...

PRAYER REQUESTS

I will be glad and
rejoice in thy mercy: for
thou hast considered my
trouble; thou hast known
my soul in adversities.

Psalm 31:7

Date:

TODAY'S PRAYER

Lord
TEACH ME TO...

*This I say then,
Walk in the Spirit, and
ye shall not fulfil the
lust of the flesh.*

Galatians 5:16

PRAYER REQUESTS

Date:

TODAY'S PRAYER

Lord
TEACH ME TO...

But my God shall supply all your need according to his riches in glory by Christ Jesus.

Philippians 4:19

PRAYER REQUESTS

Date:

TODAY'S PRAYER

Lord
TEACH ME TO...

Prayer Requests

Thy word is a lamp unto my feet, and a light unto my path.

Psalm 119:105

Date:

TODAY'S PRAYER

Lord
TEACH ME TO...

PRAYER REQUESTS

When thou passest
through the waters,
I will be with thee.
Isaiah 43:2 a

Date:

TODAY'S PRAYER

Lord
TEACH ME TO...

And so, after he
had patiently endured,
he obtained the promise.

Hebrews 6:15

PRAYER REQUESTS

Date:

TODAY'S PRAYER

Lord
TEACH ME TO...

A man's heart deviseth his way: but the Lord directeth his steps.

Proverbs 16:9

PRAYER REQUESTS

Date:

TODAY'S PRAYER

Lord
TEACH ME TO...

PRAYER REQUESTS

My flesh and my heart faileth: but God is the strength of my heart, and my portion for ever.

Psalm 73:26

Date:

TODAY'S PRAYER

Lord
TEACH ME TO...

Commit thy way unto the
Lord; trust also in him;
and he shall bring it to pass.

Psalm 37:5

PRAYER REQUESTS

Date

Lord
TEACH ME TO...

For with God nothing shall be impossible.

Luke 1:37

PRAYER REQUESTS

Date.

TODAY'S PRAYER

Lord
TEACH ME TO...

PRAYER REQUESTS

And whatsoever ye
do, do it heartily, as
to the Lord, and
not unto men.

Colossians 3:23

Date:

TODAY'S PRAYER

Lord
TEACH ME TO...

PRAYER REQUESTS

*A new commandment
I give unto you, That ye love
one another; as I have
loved you, that ye also
love one another.*

John 13:34

Date:

TODAY'S PRAYER

Lord
TEACH ME TO...

PRAYER REQUESTS

From the end of the earth will
I cry unto thee, when my heart
is overwhelmed: lead me to the
rock that is higher than I.

Psalm 61:2

Date:

TODAY'S PRAYER

Lord
TEACH ME TO...

But he that heareth,
and doeth not, is like a man
that without a foundation
built an house upon the earth

Luke 6:49

Prayer Requests

Date:

TODAY'S PRAYER

Lord
TEACH ME TO...

PRAYER REQUESTS

That if thou shalt confess with thy mouth the Lord Jesus, and shalt believe in thine heart that God hath raised him from the dead, thou shalt be saved.

Romans 10:9

Date:

TODAY'S PRAYER

_____
_____
_____
_____
_____
_____
_____
_____
_____
_____
_____
_____
_____
_____

Lord
TEACH ME TO...

_____
_____
_____
_____
_____

*Fear not: for
I am with thee.*

Isaiah 43:5

Prayer Requests

_____
_____
_____
_____
_____
_____
_____
_____
_____

Date:

TODAY'S PRAYER

Lord
TEACH ME TO...

PRAYER REQUESTS

And he said unto them,
Go ye into all the world, and
preach the gospel to
every creature.

Mark 16:15

Date.

TODAY'S PRAYER

Lord
TEACH ME TO...

I love them that love me;
and those that seek me
early shall find me.

Proverbs 8:17

Prayer Requests

Date:

TODAY'S PRAYER

Lord
TEACH ME TO...

Bless them which
persecute you: bless,
and curse not.

Romans 12:14

PRAYER REQUESTS

Date:

Lord
TEACH ME TO...

This is the day which the
Lord hath made; we will
rejoice and be glad in it.

Psalm 118:24

PRAYER REQUESTS

Date:

TODAY'S PRAYER

Lord
TEACH ME TO...

PRAYER REQUESTS

For I know the thoughts that
I think toward you, saith the Lord,
thoughts of peace, and not of evil,
to give you an expected end.

Jeremiah 29:11

Date:

TODAY'S PRAYER

Lord
TEACH ME TO...

Receive my instruction,
and not silver; and
knowledge rather
than choice gold.

Proverbs 8:10

PRAYER REQUESTS

Date:

TODAY'S PRAYER

Lord
TEACH ME TO...

Prayer Requests

Wherefore comfort
yourselves together,
and edify one another,
even as also ye do.

1 Thessalonians 5:11

Date:

TODAY'S PRAYER

_____
_____
_____
_____
_____
_____
_____
_____
_____
_____
_____
_____
_____
_____
_____
_____

In all thy ways acknowledge him, and he shall direct thy paths.

Proverbs 3:6

Lord TEACH ME TO...

_____
_____
_____
_____
_____

PRAYER REQUESTS

_____
_____
_____
_____
_____
_____
_____
_____
_____
_____
_____
_____

Date:

TODAY'S PRAYER

Lord
TEACH ME TO...

Ye are of God, little
children, and have overcome them:
because greater is he that is in you,
than he that is in the world.

1 John 4:4

Prayer Requests

Date.

TODAY'S PRAYER

Lord
TEACH ME TO...

But as for me
and my house, we will
serve the Lord.

Joshua 24:15

Prayer Requests

Date:

TODAY'S PRAYER

Lord
TEACH ME TO...

And thou shalt know
that I am the Lord: for
they shall not be ashamed
that wait for me.

Isaiah 49:23b

PRAYER REQUESTS

Date:

TODAY'S PRAYER

Lord
TEACH ME TO...

PRAYER REQUESTS

In like manner also,
that women adorn themselves
in modest apparel, with
shamefacedness and sobriety.

1 Timothy 2:9 a

Date:

Lord
TEACH ME TO...

PRAYER REQUESTS

The Lord is on my side;
I will not fear: what
can man do unto me?

Psalm 118:6

Date:

TODAY'S PRAYER

Lord
TEACH ME TO...

Prayer Requests

When a man's ways
please the Lord, he maketh
even his enemies to be
at peace with him.
Proverbs 16:7

Date.

TODAY'S PRAYER

Lord
TEACH ME TO...

PRAYER REQUESTS

And as ye would that
men should do to you,
do ye also to them likewise.

Luke 6:31

Date:

TODAY'S PRAYER

_____
_____
_____
_____
_____
_____
_____
_____
_____
_____
_____
_____
_____
_____
_____
_____
_____

Lord
TEACH ME TO...

_____
_____
_____
_____
_____

*And ye shall know
the truth, and the truth
shall make you free.*

John 8:32

Prayer Requests

_____
_____
_____
_____
_____
_____
_____
_____

Date:

TODAY'S PRAYER

Lord
TEACH ME TO...

PRAYER REQUESTS

Arise, for this matter
belongeth unto thee:
we also will be with thee:
be of good courage, and do it.

Ezra 10:4

Date:

TODAY'S PRAYER

Lord
TEACH ME TO...

Wherefore they are no
more twain, but one flesh.
What therefore God
hath joined together,
let not man put asunder.

Matthew 19:6

Prayer Requests

Date

TODAY'S PRAYER

Lord
TEACH ME TO...

PRAYER REQUESTS

She openeth her
mouth with wisdom;
and in her tongue is the
law of kindness.

Proverbs 31:26

Date:

TODAY'S PRAYER

Lord
TEACH ME TO...

Prayer Requests

In every thing give thanks: for this is the will of God in Christ Jesus concerning you.

1 Thessalonians 5:18

Date.

TODAY'S PRAYER

Lord
TEACH ME TO...

PRAYER REQUESTS

For where your
treasure is, there will
your heart be also.

Luke 12:34

Date:

TODAY'S PRAYER

Lord
TEACH ME TO...

Prayer Requests

and who knoweth whether
thou art come to the kingdom
for such a time as this?

Esther 4:14 b

Date:

TODAY'S PRAYER

Lord TEACH ME TO...

O give thanks unto the Lord; for he is good: for his mercy endureth for ever.

Psalm 136:1

PRAYER REQUESTS

Date:

TODAY'S PRAYER

Lord
TEACH ME TO...

PRAYER REQUESTS

A merry heart doeth
good like a medicine:
but a broken spirit
drieth the bones.

Proverbs 17:22

Date:

TODAY'S PRAYER

Lord
TEACH ME TO...

PRAYER REQUESTS

If ye abide in me,
and my words abide in you,
ye shall ask what ye will, and
it shall be done unto you.

John 15:7

Date:

TODAY'S PRAYER

Lord
TEACH ME TO...

Seek the Lord and his
strength, seek his face
continually.

1 Chronicles 16:11

PRAYER REQUESTS

Date:

TODAY'S PRAYER

Lord
TEACH ME TO...

But seek ye first the kingdom
of God, and his righteousness;
and all these things shall
be added unto you.

Matthew 6:33

PRAYER REQUESTS

Date.

TODAY'S PRAYER

Lord
TEACH ME TO...

Draw nigh to God,
and he will draw nigh to you.
Cleanse your hands, ye sinners;
and purify your hearts,
ye double minded.

James 4:8

Prayer Requests

Date

TODAY'S PRAYER

Lord
TEACH ME TO...

PRAYER REQUESTS

And above all things have fervent charity among yourselves: for charity shall cover the multitude of sins. Use hospitality one to another without grudging.
1 Peter 4:8-9

Date:

TODAY'S PRAYER

Lord
TEACH ME TO…

*The Lord also will be
a refuge for the oppressed, a
refuge in times of trouble.*

Psalm 9:9

Prayer Requests

Date:

Lord
TEACH ME TO...

Jesus Christ the same
yesterday, and to day,
and for ever.

Hebrews 13:8

PRAYER REQUESTS

Date:

Lord
TEACH ME TO...

PRAYER REQUESTS

Come unto me, all ye that labour and are heavy laden, and I will give you rest.

Matthew 11:28

Date:

TODAY'S PRAYER

Lord
TEACH ME TO...

PRAYER REQUESTS

Call unto me, and I will answer thee, and show thee great and mighty things, which thou knowest not.

Jeremiah 33:3

Date:

TODAY'S PRAYER

Lord
TEACH ME TO...

Prayer Requests

And, behold, I am with thee, and will keep thee in all places whither thou goest, and will bring thee again into this land.

Genesis 28:15

Date

Lord
TEACH ME TO...

Prayer Requests

I will both lay me down in peace, and sleep: for thou, Lord, only makest me dwell in safety.

Psalm 4:8

Date:

TODAY'S PRAYER

Lord
TEACH ME TO...

Prayer Requests

God is love, and he that dwelleth in love dwelleth in God, and God in him.

1 John 4:16 b

Date:

TODAY'S PRAYER

Lord
TEACH ME TO...

PRAYER REQUESTS

I will praise thee with my
whole heart: before the gods
will I sing praise unto thee.

Psalm 138:1

Date:

TODAY'S PRAYER

Lord
TEACH ME TO...

He healeth the broken in heart, and bindeth up their wounds.

Psalm 147:3

PRAYER REQUESTS

Date.

TODAY'S PRAYER

Lord TEACH ME TO...

PRAYER REQUESTS

Now faith is the substance of things hoped for, the evidence of things not seen.

Hebrews 11:1

Date:

TODAY'S PRAYER

Lord TEACH ME TO...

Who can find a virtuous woman? for her price is far above rubies. The heart of her husband doth safely trust in her, so that he shall have no need of spoil.

Proverbs 31:10-11

PRAYER REQUESTS

Date:

TODAY'S PRAYER

Lord
TEACH ME TO…

PRAYER REQUESTS

*For thou, Lord,
wilt bless the righteous, with
favour wilt thou compass
him as with a shield.*

Psalm 5:12

Date

TODAY'S PRAYER

Lord
TEACH ME TO...

Blessed are the
peacemakers: for they
shall be called the
children of God.

Matthew 5:9

PRAYER REQUESTS

Date: